Alex
and the Troll

by Clare De Marco and Andy Elkerton

W

First published in 2011 by
Franklin Watts
338 Euston Road
London
NW1 3BH

Franklin Watts Australia
Level 17/207 Kent Street
Sydney
NSW 2000

A CIP catalogue record for this book is available
from the British Library.

ISBN 978 0 7496 9478 4 (pbk)

Series Editor: Jackie Hamley
Series Advisor: Catherine Glavina
Series Designer: Peter Scoulding

Printed in China

Franklin Watts is a divison of
Hachette Children's Books,
an Hachette UK company.
www.hachette.co.uk

One day, Alex and his dad
built a bridge.

Next morning,
Alex got a surprise.

There was a troll under his bridge!

5

The troll jumped out. He was big and ugly, and he smelt of rotten cabbages.

"Who's that trip-trapping over my bridge?" growled the troll.

"Excuse me, but it's my bridge," said Alex.

"It's my bridge now!"
replied the troll.

"But I built it with my dad,"
said Alex.

"Well I'm not leaving," the troll roared. "It's near the swamp and it smells perfect."

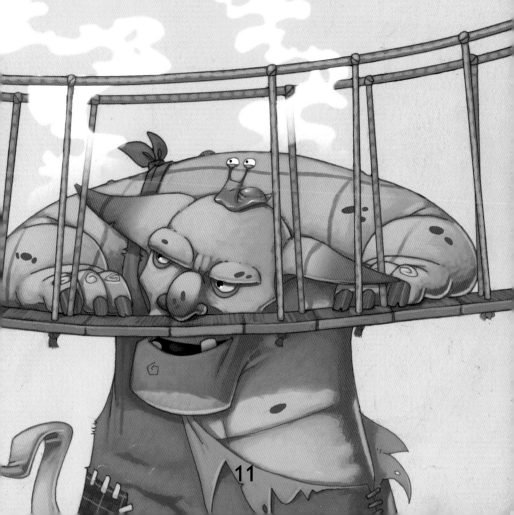

Alex stomped home.
He thought about how
to get rid of the troll.

"The troll likes the bridge because it smells of the swamp," thought Alex.

Alex had an idea. He went into the garden and filled up his wheelbarrow.

Alex tiptoed back to his bridge.

The troll was snoring
loudly.

Quietly, Alex put flower pots all over his bridge.

Soon, the troll woke up
with a big snort.

"Who's that trip-trapping over my bridge?" he spluttered.

Then the troll started
to sneeze.

"Yuck!" he yelled. "It smells disgusting here!"

The troll jumped into the
stream and splashed away.

"That got rid of him!"
laughed Alex.

Puzzle 1

Put these pictures in the correct order.
Now tell the story in your own words.
How short can you make the story?

annoyed   cross

excited

kind   mean

smelly

Choose the words which best describe each character. Can you think of any more? Pretend to be one of the characters!

Answers

Puzzle 1

The correct order is:

1d, 2e, 3a, 4f, 5b, 6c

Puzzle 2

Alex   The correct words are annoyed, cross.

The incorrect word is excited.

Troll   The correct words are mean, smelly.

The incorrect word is kind.

Look out for more Leapfrog stories:

For details of all our titles go to: www.franklinwatts.co.uk

*hardback